THE TRAIN BOOK

illustrated by John Johnson

MERRIGOLD PRESS • NEW YORK

© 1970 Merrigold Press, Racine, Wisconsin 53402. All rights reserved.
Printed in the U.S.A. No part of this book may be reproduced or copied
in any form without written permission from the publisher.
All trademarks are the property of Merrigold Press. ISBN: 0-307-03916-1
A B C D E F G H I J K L M

The railroad yard is a busy place.
Chug-chug, puff-puff. Listen to the
engines getting ready to go.

The railroad workers get up early each day.
"Good morning," says the conductor.

This big engine will pull the train.
The engineer is ready to drive.

There's a car to carry coal and a flatcar to carry a van.

The brakeman will connect them.

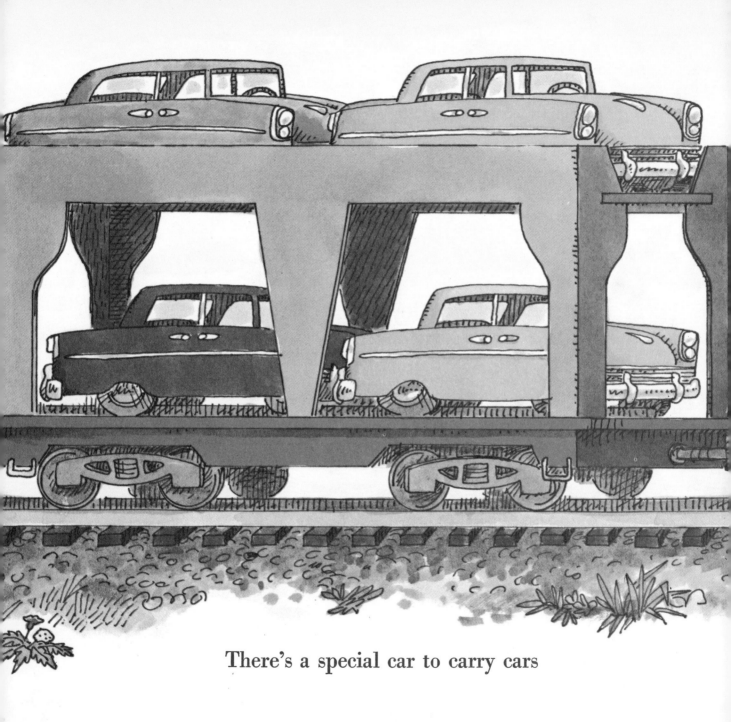

There's a special car to carry cars

and one to carry oil.

These boxcars are loaded with big boxes and packages.

Here's the passenger car. It carries people.

"All aboard!"

"Watch your step," says the conductor.

Then he punches all the tickets.

At dinner time the passengers eat in the dining car.

When they get sleepy, they sleep in berths
in the Pullman car.

And all night long the train will go—
through new towns and over bridges.

It goes across the countryside and through tunnels.
See the friendly people wave hello!

The red caboose is the
last one down the track.
Clickety-clack, clickety-clack.
Listen to the sound as it
hurries down the track.